# EAST LONDON POETS

Edited By Brixie Payne

First published in Great Britain in 2018 by:

 Young**Writers**

Young Writers
Remus House
Coltsfoot Drive
Peterborough
PE2 9BF
Telephone: 01733 890066
Website: www.youngwriters.co.uk

# FOREWORD

Young Writers was created in 1991 with the express purpose of promoting and encouraging creative writing. Each competition we create is tailored to the relevant age group, hopefully giving each child the inspiration and incentive to create their own piece of writing, whether it's a poem or a short story. We truly believe that seeing it in print gives pupils a sense of achievement and pride in their work and themselves.

Our latest competition, Monster Poetry, focuses on uncovering the different techniques used in poetry and encouraging pupils to explore new ways to write a poem. Using a mix of imagination, expression and poetic styles, this anthology is an impressive snapshot of the inventive, original and skilful writing of young people today. These poems showcase the creativity and talent of these budding new writers as they learn the skills of writing, and we hope you are as entertained by them as we are.

# CONTENTS

Aidan Waugh (8) — 58
Faramoluwa Ogunde (8) — 60
Sophie Dolan (8) — 61
Mbangala Green (8) — 62
Kalifa Dennis (7) — 63
Honey Dye (7) — 64
Freya Sofia Mahomudally (8) — 65
Daria Maria Ailenei (9) — 66
Ayaan Shaikh (8) — 67
Michael Tsidi (8) — 68
Iman Muhammed (8) — 69
Adam Tuc (8) — 70
Maya Juliana Bryan (9) — 71
Samuel Barnard (7) — 72
Dogan Dag (8) — 73
Tyler Allbeury (8) — 74
Callum Gill (8) — 75
Jenna Ghelleahe (8) — 76
Bailee Lewis (8) — 77
Daniel Pemaj (8) — 78
Titot Guillaume (7) — 79
Sana Bhaiji (8) — 80
Tyra Alcin (8) — 81
Quinton Lamptey (8) — 82
Ata Ozan Cetin (8) — 83
Austin Gustainis (7) — 84
Aarman Malipatil (7) — 85
Florrie Irish (7) — 86
Aiden O'Hara (8) — 87
Josie Knight (7) — 88
Ami Johnston (8) — 89
Jaya Mander (8) — 90
Kaya Hamit (8) — 91
Shiv Patel (8) — 92
Asia Karmelle Yau Philip (8) — 93
Imogen Benjamin (8) — 94
Skye Spence (8) — 95
Chris Frangou (8) — 96
Shai Davis (8) — 97
Madison Drew Colley (7) — 98
Matthew Porter (8) — 99
Ruby Treviss (8) — 100
Lily Rose Slack (8) — 101

Ari Ash (7) — 102
Reuben Carr (8) — 103
Louis Grant (8) — 104

## Marion Richardson Primary School, Stepney

Samira Akhter (7) — 105
Maria Akthar (7) — 106
Aafia Bint Tufail (7) — 107
Abdullah Ahmad (7) — 108
Idris Drici (6) — 109

## North Beckton Primary School, Beckton

Holly Bai (10) — 110
Alexander Naydenov (9) — 111
Amélie Afia Owusu-Gyamfi (9) — 112
Sumayyah Rarih (9) — 113
Ioana Potinteu (7) — 114
Faariah Malik (11) — 115
Ziyad Shiraz Ahmed (8) — 116
Rayan Thummanah (9) — 117
Riana Rahman (9) — 118
Maysa Popa Sayed (9) — 120
Maheru Uddin (10) — 121
Lily Sobiye-Kotwica (8) — 122
Viktoria Strupnenska (9) — 123
Nicolas Kulczewski (9) — 124
Inaaya Ahmed (9) — 125
Manoor Ali Sajjad (8) — 126
Weronika Miśta (10) — 127
Chantelle Oduro-Donkor (8) — 128
Mahmoud Bachrouch (9) — 129
Qais (10) — 130
Kamila Baran (9) — 131
Vyte Lukosiute (9) — 132
Zayne Joaquin-Wayne Boggs (7) — 133
Nicole Kamila Rompca (9) — 134
Daniel (10) — 135

## Selwyn Primary School, London

| | |
|---|---|
| Rania Bendjebbas (10) | 136 |
| Zachary Grant (10) | 137 |
| Joshua Hollows (8) | 138 |
| Elisa Ali (9) | 139 |
| Jason Vijayendra (7) | 140 |

## St James' CE Junior School, Forest Gate

| | |
|---|---|
| Roshni Pithiya (7) | 141 |
| Tej Paresh Gohil (8) | 142 |
| Umar Hassan Mallu (9) | 144 |
| Kirsty Asamoah (8) | 146 |
| Zeba (9) | 147 |
| Nisha Kaur (9) | 148 |
| Sienna Sylvia Byne (9) | 149 |
| Kayla Monica Monteiro (9) | 150 |
| Daddy Dampha (9) | 151 |
| Gabriella Mumenu Kinduku (9) | 152 |
| Siyona Paliwal (9) | 153 |
| Hajar Bennebri (9) | 154 |
| Matyas Sarosi (9) | 155 |
| Yahyah Islam (9) | 156 |
| Aisha Saddiq (9) | 157 |
| Fabian Hurduc (8) | 158 |
| Favour Odunola Akinwande (9) | 159 |
| Raenella Ofori (8) | 160 |
| Tayyab Ahmed Hussain (9) | 161 |
| Sara Abdo (9) | 162 |
| Henriqueta Djalo (9) | 163 |
| Anayet Noor (9) | 164 |
| Miftahul Islam (9) | 165 |
| Mohammed-Quam Temitope Balogun (9) | 166 |

## St John Of Jerusalem CE Primary School, Hackney

| | |
|---|---|
| Nathan Precilla (8) | 167 |
| Wen-Jie Zheng (8) | 168 |
| Chinedu Duru (8) | 169 |
| Edward Skrine (8) | 170 |

## St Matthias CE Primary School, London

| | |
|---|---|
| Tahiya Ahmed (8) | 171 |

## Whittingham Primary Academy, Walthamstow

| | |
|---|---|
| Mary Luggie (9) | 172 |
| Maimuna Ali Mohamed (10) | 174 |
| Mohammod Dua Mahmud Unnoto (9) | 176 |
| Chloe Alexandra Bray (9) | 177 |
| Ellie-Mae Carroll (9) | 178 |
| Richard Khalil Minott (11) | 180 |
| Antonia Maria Avram (9) | 182 |
| Daniel Brace Carmona (9) | 183 |
| Summer Yakici (10) | 184 |
| Taybah Zainab Shah (9) | 185 |
| Nathaniel Marcus Kai Thomas (10) | 186 |
| Emmanuel Chibuike Chinedu (8) | 187 |
| Erhan Bulut (8) | 188 |
| Laurynas Vaicenavicius (9) | 189 |
| Ali Dereli (9) | 190 |
| Rehan Mohamed (9) | 191 |

# THE POEMS

# Back From School

When I was back from school I met,
A monster, hairy and blue
With teeth sharp and white,
It wasn't a scary fright.

When I was home, I asked Mum,
If I could keep him,
She said, "First, give him a trim."
When Dad was out back,
We could smell the BBQ.

The monster, which was hairy,
Stepped on my toy ferry,
But I didn't mind at all,
Because I was back from school.

## Avril Nakibirango Luyindi (10)

# A Monster Invention

Quick! Read this poem!
It's waiting just for you,
A tale of a unique inventor,
Who is also a monster, it's true.

It started with a girl called Wendy,
Who was poking around Rhossili Bay,
When beyond the mist she spotted,
A pink, fluffy monster sobbing in a cave.

"Why do you cry so loudly?"
Wendy curiously asked,
"Everyone laughs at me and my inventions,"
replied the monster,
"And they make me feel daft."

"Well show me your creation," Wendy said softly,
So the monster stepped towards her machine
And explained that it was 'The Vegetator',
A machine to help kids eat their greens.

All you had to do was say your favourite food,
Then pull the lever to the max,
And out would come a yummy, healthy snack.

"Let's pull this thing on to the beach!" Wendy
exclaimed,
Then everyone came rushing to see the weird
wonder,
One by one, everyone had a turn,
Gallons of greens were gobbled by the youngsters.

So the monster felt joyful, everyone loved her art,
And suddenly an idea came crashing into her head,
Her next invention would be the world's biggest
sunglasses,
"Come on Wendy, join in!"

## Ashira Ayinke Odutola (7)

# Mean To Nice

My name is Globby.
I was born in a deep, dark cave
under the grounds of Monster Island.
I had some bright yellow teeth
and one long monster tooth.
My eyes were as red as roses
and my body's hair was as blue as the sky.
Also, I had three very beady eyes.
I was very selfish
and loved to cause loads of drama.
One day there was a whirling circle.
I jumped in and ended up in the human world.
I met very nice friends and they taught me how to be nice
but unfortunately, I ended up back in Monster Island.
Everyone absolutely adored the nicer and newer Globby.
They loved my first ever smile.
My mouth widened and everyone got a glimpse of my bright yellow teeth...
and don't forget monster tooth!

## Joyce Ferandes (9)
Ainslie Wood Primary School, Chingford

# TTTulie Finds The End...

TTTulie wants a friend.
She goes through the sewers and finds the end.
TTTulie finds a friend and their friendship will never end.

TTTulie, TTTulie, what have you done?
You stink and you're crazy like my Aunt Tum.
TTTulie, you've gone mad.
Toes are what you smell of 'cause you stink so bad.

What is your first name, middle and last?
Toilet? Tech? Tickle? Time?
TTTulie finds a friend.
TTTulie finds the end.
Through the maze until she finds the magical wonders of a friend.
TTTulie finds a friend, but then finds she's at the end.

## Isis-Li Logan (9)

Ainslie Wood Primary School, Chingford

# ZY-Borg The Half Robot Monster

"ZY, why are you half robot?
Are you from Borgey?"
"Yes," replied ZY.
"Are your biceps metal?"
"No," said ZY.
"Borgey people aren't robots."
"Yes I know that," said ZY.
"Borgey people are monster bears."
"Yes I know that too and..." said ZY.
"I have a question for you..."
"What is it?"
"I'm getting my robot half removed!" exclaimed ZY.
"Okay I get the message,
I'll get lost!"

## Imaad ud Din (9)
Ainslie Wood Primary School, Chingford

# A Monster Called Binky

There was a monster called Binky
But everybody called him Stinky.
He hated his life.
He had no wife.
He made everybody sad
and everybody got mad.
But one day he changed,
he got a lovely wife.
He had a wonderful life.
Everybody called him Binky
(apart from one boy who called him Stinky).
He lived happily ever after,
until one day somebody called him Pinky.
Binky said, "It's alright, I love pink!"
And from then on everybody called him Pinky.

**Polina Vasylyeva (10)**
Ainslie Wood Primary School, Chingford

# Disaster

There once was a mermaid who lived in a lake.
She had hair just like snakes.
Her name was Eliza.
She had a designer.

Could you think of a better name
For this girl who was insane?
How about Disaster?
That's her new name.
I bet she gives you goosebumps.

Now it's about time to sleep
When it's time to count sheep.
Disaster was sleeping,
She heard a big crash!
I wonder what that crash was?
Maybe The Flash!

## Amy Lane (9)
Ainslie Wood Primary School, Chingford

# The King Of Serpents

The king of serpents gives a mighty scare
As it can only kill you with a stare
The king of serpents matches no other
Except for the Basilisk, its brother

Only the Heir of the Glare
Can summon the nightmare
So enemies of the Heir beware
Otherwise you'll experience the murderous stare

It petrifies you with its reflection
And shows no loving affection
It lives for centuries
And gives people horrible memories

But it can die
By the chicken's cry.

## Elena Jiang (10)
Ainslie Wood Primary School, Chingford

# Mature Monster

There is a monster who is mature
and when he sleeps he does a huge snore.
He is so funny that his friends think he is an
actual bunny.

He is very kind and loving
and he loves hugging.
He loves to play games
but they are all the same.

He doesn't like being lonely
because he doesn't feel homely.
He has a sister that calls him Mister.

**Star Keeble (9)**
Ainslie Wood Primary School, Chingford

# The Flicker Of The Monster

Flicker
The body of the beast is all I can see.
Flicker
The curved mountains moved alongside me.
Flicker
A furry junkyard that flinches beyond the sea.

And in only a flicker, new shapes appear
And in only movements, I contribute to my fears.
And so a fast flinching shapeshifter is all I can see,
And now a fast flinching shapeshifter drags me so I can be free...

## Zonera Ibrahim (9)
Ainslie Wood Primary School, Chingford

# Jeremy The Jelly

Jeremy was wobbly
As well as very knobbly.
He was also very wibbly
And walked down the streets weakly.

Jeremy was poky
And his voice was very croaky.
He was very sticky
So you must walk past him quickly.

Jeremy's eyes were googly
And also very spooky.
Jeremy was jelly
And also was very smelly.

## Aaishah Siddiq (9)
Ainslie Wood Primary School, Chingford

# It's New Friend

On a sunny day
Which was in May,
It, the monster, went to play
In the grass and in the hay.

There he saw a child
Who was completely wild.
The child saw It,
He wanted to give him a hit.

It seemed to be rapid and funny,
Also he smelt like honey,
Furry and had huge horns,
They hurt like thorns.

Worriedly, the child ran home,
Where he was no longer alone.
He couldn't believe how his day had been,
Everything felt like a dream.

**Karina Palkowska (9)**
Barn Croft Primary School, Walthamstow

# Non-Bullypuss

One night when the sun went down
and the sky outside was brown,
I heard a noise
coming from my pile of toys
and out came Non-Bullypuss.

He's friendly
but ten times more deadly
to bullies at least.
I knew I had been bad at school,
I just wanted to be cool.

He came towards my bed,
in a second I would be dead.
I knew I had no hope,
I had said rude words to the Pope.
Non-Bullypuss was out to get me!

He opened up his suitcase.
*Clang!* went my toy mace.
I couldn't turn and race,
there was greed on his despicable face.
Non-Bullypuss was out to get me!

Non-Bullypuss was out to get me!
I was in a big mess, see?
Non-Bullypuss was out to get me!
He was going to mess with me!

## Moss Cubit McSweeney (9)
Barn Croft Primary School, Walthamstow

# How I Got Shelly

One day
I have to say
I had not plenty,
My fridge was empty,
So I needed to go to the shops!

But when I arrived there...
There was a little fella,
In the window.

I asked the shopkeeper,
He gave it to me for free.

"What should I do with you?"
I whispered to him.
"Bee!" he said.
He dribbled on me.

So I took him home,
Forgetting about my empty fridge.
On the way he saw an It.
It said, "Hi!"

My poor fella got startled
And started to cry.

I took him in my arms
And walked home.
"Bye," said It.

At home I called him Shelly,
We both watched telly...
Bye!

## Fatima Chishtie (9)
Barn Croft Primary School, Walthamstow

# Craven's First Day In The Kitchen

Craven works in the kitchen
for soon he will be licking.

He cooks the dinner and takes a taste,
cuts the vegetables, stuffs it down,
uses his wings to reheat the oven,
eats the meat with his talons.

Make sure not to hire this guy
for you will find out what's inside.

Uses human bones to make the soup,
breaks its egg to make the breakfast.

Make sure not to try its soup
or your stomach will have eternal doom!

**Deimantas Ramonas (9)**
Barn Croft Primary School, Walthamstow

# Things Found In My Monster's Mouth

A hand with a band.
A bin with a shark fin.
I cannot believe this but... a rug with a pug.
Glue filled with goo.
A shoe with poo.
There's more to go...
Shark fins and metal pins.
Children's bones, stolen phones.
A giant house, a little mouse.
Eleven frogs.
A hundred dogs.
A nut and a hut.
I just cannot believe this... OMG!
A giant cat in a little hat.
Don't say or she is going to scratch you!

**Mia Tadla (8)**
Barn Croft Primary School, Walthamstow

# My Monster's Fur Coat

Cagton has a big coat
He uses it to hide things
And every time I try to look
He goes ahead and scares me.
One day he left his coat
And here's what I found...

A comb to brush it.
A rusty hook.
A spare eyeball
(Just in case he loses one).
A nail as dirty as mud.
A giant monster egg.
A stolen horn.
His sharp fangs.
Fresh cooked beef
And warm soup.
Oh no, I've been caught, noooo!

## Cameron Smith (9)
Barn Croft Primary School, Walthamstow

# The Devilator's Day On The Beach

One day a monster fell from the sky,
I really hope he does not die.

I asked him if he was going to cry,
I really hope he does not lie.

Now we go to the beach,
I hope he has no bleach.

We also scare people,
When they're on a steeple.

Then we go and buy
Some fish and chips, oh my!

It is fun coming from the sky,
Even though I cannot fly.

## Marlowe Conochie-Barker (9)
Barn Croft Primary School, Walthamstow

# Planet Bleem

Vicky Cookie Kal,
The three-eyed monster
Lives on Planet Bleem,
Where all monsters beam,
They are all...

Fantastically funny,
They hop like bunnies.

Very clever,
They love wearing leather.

Child lovers,
Nice huggers.

They love eating veggies
And like being edgy.

Sweet sharers
But not big scarers.

**Dakota Monika Kavaliauskaite (9)**
Barn Croft Primary School, Walthamstow

# Spiky

Spiky is unusual
and mostly cruel!

He has rotten teeth
because he eats too much beef.
A colourful body,
not too shoddy.

Child eater.
Bone beater.
Big cheater.
Not a friendly greeter.

Bad breath.
Bad as death.
Loves gum.
Amazingly dumb.

Hates a run.
Hates all fun!

**Joshua Gomez Moore (8)**
Barn Croft Primary School, Walthamstow

# Monster Meany Went To The Shop

He bought...
a slithering slug
and a big bug.

A plastic jug,
and he saw a pug.

Then he gave a big shrug,
he felt a bug.

Then he said, "I want a big bed,"
but it was too much.

What about a shed?
Then be bought some bread
then he bled!

**Jann Seddon (8)**
Barn Croft Primary School, Walthamstow

# Cool Jeff, The Monster

He's friendly
but sometimes deadly.
He's furious
but sometimes curious.
He's spiky
but sometimes stripy.
He's creepy
but sometimes sleepy.
He's really ugly
but sometimes rather fumbly.
He's silly
but he likes his friend, Billy.

## David Olech-Barqueiro (9)
Barn Croft Primary School, Walthamstow

# Gobbly Wobbly Slime Man!

Slimy as my saliva.
Hairy as a lion's mane.
Colourful as a rainbow.
Clever as a scary yeti.
The five-eyed, fat, ugly monster.
The giant four-fanged creature.
Sweet as a lollipop.
Fierce as a tiger wrestling.

That's the Gobbly Wobbly Slime Man!

## Eve Catlin (9)

Barn Croft Primary School, Walthamstow

# Hideous Haunting Hilly

Petrifying character.
Hideous fanger.

Terrible hider.
Super sighter.

Terrifying diet.
Heaven forbid he's never quiet.

Angry like a screaming teacher.
Stinky like odour.

Bad as an old sewer.
A twenty-five eyed monster.

## Neda Stanekzi (9)
Barn Croft Primary School, Walthamstow

# My Monster

My monster is really funny
And quite a dummy.

He likes the park
But hates the dark.

He has a big life
And a terrible wife.

He's as silly as a clown
And as busy as a town.

My monster's name is the Five-Eyed Cow.

## Herbie Cross (8)
Barn Croft Primary School, Walthamstow

# The Kid Hunter's Day At Work

The Kid Hunter went to work
But he accidentally burped.

When he sat down at his desk
He was a mess.

The Kid Hunter's shift was over.
He wanted to see his dog, Oliver.

When he felt bored
He wanted to practise with his sword.

## Rohans Conosa (9)
Barn Croft Primary School, Walthamstow

# The Shape-Shifter

She was born in the ocean,
Fur as white as snow,
Eyes as dark as the night,
Scars on her face,
That represent the threats that have come to her.

She is as tough as a tiger on the outside,
She is as soft as a pillow on the inside,
She loves singing,
Her dream is to be as famous as her sister,
Her other dream is to write poetry.

Her mum and dad are monsters too,
Her friends are almost like her,
But when they're sad, they turn black,
And she turns grey.

When they're happy, they turn into unicorns,
And shoot rainbows out of their horns,
They love shopping,
They have a closet full of clothes they love.

**Amie Sonko (8)**
Buxton School, Leytonstone

# Shortie

Shortie was first found in the ocean,
But then she escaped,
She only had one eye,
And she was lots of fun to play with.

Although she was short,
She loved running,
She was green,
And glowed in the dark.

She had no teeth,
Her tongue was blue,
She was really nice and kind.

However, if she didn't get what she wanted,
She was rude,
And always in a bad mood.

**Folabomi Faleye (9)**
Buxton School, Leytonstone

# The Slime Monster

In the depths of Hell, a monster was born,
Not just any monster, a slime monster,
He would go from town to town,
Looking for... slime!

But by looking for slime,
He was wasting his time,
He needed to eat.

He was blue with purple eyes,
And one eye patch,
His scent left a trail of betrayal.

Legend has it, he was betrayed,
By someone he loved,
But who?

## Cyan Morrison (11) & Mya
Buxton School, Leytonstone

# Deadly Monster

My name is Deadly Dave,
I'm a bad monster,
I turn animals to devils!

I live in the dark forest,
My devil friends live with me,
I'm really fluffy, hairy and smelly.

My horns are very sharp,
And I have bloody teeth,
On my head, I have a crack.

I'm really scary,
But people try to steal my soul,
And they try to kill me!

**Juwariyah Moe (8)**
Buxton School, Leytonstone

# Piju The Fast

Down from the sky,
From the deep, blue sky he came,
Fast and smiling, all shining,
His name was Piju,
He came to Earth to find new friends,
And he found me!

We went on a ride,
High up into the sky,
His friends were the planets and the stars,
We went to play with the sun,
And when we got tired,
We listened to the moon's bedtime stories.

I fell into a sleep so sweet,
I dreamt about my friend, Piju,
About his three shiny eyes,
And his funny smile.

I woke up in my bed,
Early in the morning,
But I knew that that night,
There would be another new adventure...

**Ivan Vasilev (9)**
Buxton School, Leytonstone

34

# The Fire Dragon

The Fire Dragon was smirking,
As he blew every plant and animal to dust,
He then met me.

I asked him, "Are you going to burn me?"
The Fire Dragon started burning everything I had
I shouted, "Stop!"
But the dragon kept on going.

I showered water onto it,
The dragon soon turned to dust,
The next day, I was handed an award,
Everyone cheered.

## Ziqra Masahudu (8)
Buxton School, Leytonstone

# Daisy And Friends

Daisy was from Mars,
Daisy and her friends went on lots of adventures.
She was good and friendly,
But a boy called Mekhi was being rude,
To her and her friends.

Daisy was planning revenge,
She was going to teach him a lesson,
By locking him in a room,
And leaving him there for an hour
So next time, he won't be rude to Daisy!

**Hannah Kehinde Joseph (9)**
Buxton School, Leytonstone

# Tina The Monster

Tina the monster wept and cried,
She tried to make friends, she tried and tried
Then came along a girl called Daisy,
But she was very, very lazy,
Tina came to the conclusion that making friends
was hard,
So she made a large thing in the backyard,
It turned out to be a robot friend!

## Naomi Taiwo Joseph (9)
Buxton School, Leytonstone

# Cute Monsters

**M** onsters are cool, funny and fluffy.

**O** ddie is a cute, kind and fluffy monster.

**N** one of the other humans are his friends, but I am.

**S** ome monsters say that he is the cleverest monster in Monster Land.

**T** he monster friends that he has are very kind to him.

**E** veryone in his family loves him.

**R** ob, his monster friend, plays with Oddie every day.

**Ivelina Kavazova (9)**
Buxton School, Leytonstone

# Mr Goggle Goes To The Park

Mr Goggle was wriggling down the street,
To meet his best friend, Geets,
So that they could go to the iglo park,
But he heard a monster bark,
Geets ran away,
So Mr Goggle had to save the day!
Mr Goggle went up to the monster,
And told the monster to stop,
Then Geets came back,
And all day they played in their sacks.

**Maleah Bangura (9)**
Buxton School, Leytonstone

# Monster Goes To School

Oogie loved to learn,
But he had no friends,
Because he kept getting bullied,
My monster went to school every day,
And he was never late,
Oogie loved maths,
But he didn't like bullies,
My monster spoke English.

## Tiarna-Marie Thompson (8)
Buxton School, Leytonstone

# Fuzz Ball

Fuzzball; big, bad and scary.
Everyone around him feels a little weary.
Big dragon wings and talons like a hawk's.
Everyone hides wherever he walks.

Fuzzball; ferocious, formidable face, frightening.
His speed as fast as a streak of lightning.
Whenever he roars people cower in fear.
One by one they shed a tear.

Fuzzball; seeming bad but actually misunderstood.
His heart is truly good.
For in his heart, in his heart lies loyalty and
kindness.
Others believe it's polluted with darkness.

So as he watches others play
He tries to change every day.
To reflect what's inside
But in his body, the true monster resides.

## Saif Ahmed (9)
Cayley Primary School, London

# Just Imagine

Just imagine you were on a mythical planet called Pandora and you saw a slimy, stinky, smelly, sneaky monster called Globby.

What would you do?

Just imagine he was going to attack you, what would you do?

Would you attack Globby or be nice?

Just imagine monsters are real then you have to say they have feelings too.

Don't be horrible and mean to someone because they have rights too.

Girls and boys are equal.

It does not matter if you're fat or skinny, have different skin colours, it matters about how you feel because everyone is unique in their own way. My message is... Just imagine.

## Unadhy Yusrah Insaan (11)
Cayley Primary School, London

# Zee, My Fighter

I was looking outside from the window,
When I heard a little hello.
I turned around and it looked a little yellow.
It looked mellow too.
I said softly, "Who are you?"
He replied happily, "I am Zee!
I love to play! Can I play with you?"
I was excited so I replied with a, "Yes, you may!"
Then suddenly darkness had struck.
A red-eyed monster that looked like muck
Then Zee looked at him and said, "Yuck!"
Zee started battling and fighting him
Until the monster went back to migrating.
Oh I love you Zee!

## Khadija Rahman (10)
Cayley Primary School, London

# About Sticky

Hi, my name is Sticky,
My language is called Icky.
I love watching Mickey,
Wait, I feel so itchy.
I have a brother called Mitchy,
And a sister called Stitchy.
I never heard of this name
Until I found out about a game.
I'm trying to find a villain,
His name is Tillan,
He has a brother called Dillan.
I know that rhyming is criming
But there is nothing else to do.
Oh, I forgot to say I love to moo.
Argh! Oh sorry, my sister just said, "Boo!"

## Hasna Nazifa (8)
Cayley Primary School, London

# Invisible Thumbisivle

Invisible Thumbisivle, prettiest monster you could
ever find.
Invisible Thumbisivle, one of a kind.

Invisible Thumbisivle, size of a thumb.
Invisible Thumbisivle, ever so numb.

Invisible Thumbisivle, turns invisible when scared.
Invisible Thumbisivle, always there.

Invisible Thumbisivle, watches like a hawk.
Invisible Thumbisivle, rarely talks.

Invisible Thumbisivle, feels like cotton candy.
Invisible Thumbisivle, has a friend called Sandy.

## Ghania Sonia Abdallah (10)
Cayley Primary School, London

# The Deadly Labyrinth

Once there was a monster that listened when you had something to say.
Just write to him or talk to him if you or anyone is hurt.
Don't delay, come to him to make the day.
There was an abandoned cave so his friend ran away while the other boys came to play.
But then his friend ended up in a labyrinth.
In the middle was a Minotaur that eats you alive.
As the friend entered the middle Furball jumped in and got eaten.
As his friend ran away he said, "I want to play."

## Ayat Arshia Khan (8)
Cayley Primary School, London

# Fatty Pat The Fubsy

To the spiders and the ants he's as fat as a human
eye.
But for a gardener, Fatty Pat is a small disaster.
He's silly and smelly
and has a big belly
and is fond of mustard and mousse.

His nickname is Fubsy.
He chews on ants with his tiny teeth that clench
like a hedgehog.

But when it's feeling naughty
it likes to gobble flowers.
And something else,
Fatty Pat is naughty because he never showers.

## Shafiq Shaaban (8)
Cayley Primary School, London

# Volingaa

There's a monster about
and he's hideous and ugly.
He's a one-eyed beast.
He likes to feast
which makes him look angry.
He wobbles and jiggles on the spot
and he's slimy, slobby and cool.
When he sees a person he goes all hot, like the
burning sun.
(Yeah, very cool!)
However, he is friendly to everyone
and he likes to run.
His name is Volingaa and he's unique
and he likes to have some fun!

## Sumayya Chowdhury (10)
Cayley Primary School, London

# My Monster Ruined Homework

My monster ruined my homework,
He is very slim and greedy.
My monster turned out to be a jerk,
He ruined the adoption papers.
Now I am stuck with him.
He is a pain in the butt.
He's stupid and careless now,
He says, "Pow!"
So I would go adopt him.
He named himself Kim.
Sorry, he's dumb.
I am sure he will be a pain in the bum!

## Hamzah Al-Hassan (9)
Cayley Primary School, London

# Rainbow Fluff

Once there lived a beautiful monster called
Rainbow and she was as fluffy as a cloud.
So that's why people called her Rainbow Fluff.
One day when she woke up she went to the shops
and people called her ugly, she began to cry.
She asked people, "Am I ugly?"
When she got home she looked in the mirror
and saw she was rainbow-coloured!

## Nusayba-Eleni Chowdhury (9)
Cayley Primary School, London

# Dangerous

Your corn horns are as yellow as the sun.
Your bright pink lips are as bright as the sea
and as fun as the sun.
Your cute cheeks are as chunky as cheese.
You creep under my bed when I sleep.
I thought I saw a monster underneath my chair.
Her face was purple and she had pink hair.

## Nusaibah Simin Aika (9)
Cayley Primary School, London

# The Late Monster

My monster is cute,
But he is very mute,
He is very hairy,
But he's very scary.

He looks friendly,
But he is very unfriendly,
His name is Zog,
Who likes to eat frogs.

He is very rude,
But he's a cool dude,
Monsters want to hug him,
But he wants to run from them,
He likes to fight,
But only in the light.

I think he is very kind,
But everyone thinks he's unkind,
I like him because he's cute.

But he doesn't like monsters calling him cute,
He will get angry and fight,
But only in the light.

Everyone calls him Zog
Who likes to eat frogs!

## Manveer Kasba (8)
Lime Academy Larkswood, Chingford

# The Merman Chloe

The night is dark, deep down in the sea,
Out of the corner of my eye, I see something
peeking at me,
My body is shaking, who can it be?

The teeth are as sharp as the blade of a knife,
The big, beady eyes stare at me mysteriously,
The pink, scaly tail shimmers in the only ray of
light,
She swims closer and closer,
A chill goes down my spine.

When all of a sudden, *bam!*
A gush of laughter comes towards me,
"Ha ha! I win!" she says loudly,
Word after word, she talks speedily.

She's friendly and nice to the people she finds,
We play for hours and hours on end,
Everything about her is perfect and lovely,
A kind heart is all that I see.

## Maria Rahman (7)
Lime Academy Larkswood, Chingford

# Gebbler

Gebbler the monster, came wandering back
sobbing,
"Gebbler, why are you sobbing, fellow?"
"I can't read, my mentor, I want to be able to read,
So I can say anything I want to anyone."
"I will teach you how to read,
But you need to be quiet, please."

Gebbler said, "Okay," and walked away,
Waiting until it was the next day
He woke up the next day all refreshed,
Thinking to himself, *I will do my best*.

As Gebbler met the other monster again,
He started to read his first story,
And said, "I need all the glory!"
Finally, Gebbler was able to read,
The other monster said,
"Finally, now I can leave!"

## Debby Tesfai (8)
Lime Academy Larkswood, Chingford

# Monster And Me

My friendly monster is fluffy and soft,
In the dark, he helps me see,
And when I sleep,
He keeps an eye on me.

When in my room,
I play and I pray,
So I can be happy every day,
It's my monster and me throughout the day,
He helps me, he's okay.

Time to go to bed,
It's all dark and quiet,
But who wants to sleep?
Definitely not me,
I'm not tired, I'm not sleepy,
I'm very hungry.

I feel like a monster most of the time,
Now my eyes feel heavy,
I feel so tired,
Monster and I will now sleep through the night,
Goodnight.

## Angelica Georgiou (7)
Lime Academy Larkswood, Chingford

# The Stinkiest Monster On Earth

The Stinkiest was born in a potato,
He had green skin and rainbow eyes,
He stunk so he had no friends.

He left the potato to explore the world,
And met a monster on a volcano,
He could not believe his eyes,
Because he'd met the best monster in the world.

He asked, "Will you be my friend forever?"
And then he pushed him because he said no,
"I'm sorry I pushed you, please come back!"
And he ended up with a friend.

His friend was a very stinky monster,
He was just like him,
And they were best friends forever,
From then on, they both had a shower every day,
So they were nice and clean!

## Robin Tilki (8)
Lime Academy Larkswood, Chingford

# Bloop The Gloop

Bloop the Gloop
With his shiny, shaggy hair
Scuttles around Earth
As if he just doesn't care

Bloop the Gloop
With his four huge eyes
If you see him at night
You will get a surprise

Bloop the Gloop
With his two wobbly tentacles
Some people might think
He is made of chemicals

Bloop the Gloop
Is short and round
Be careful you don't stand on him
When he's walking on the ground

Bloop the Gloop
Is really rather stinky
He bathes once a year
And thinks that's plenty!

## Aidan Waugh (8)
Lime Academy Larkswood, Chingford

# Dragonray's Rampage

Dragonray, Dragonray,
He's on a rampage,
He may come to eat you,
He may come to beat you,
Or he may just come to eat your beetroot.

He may fireball your place,
And will ruin your race,
He may eat your prawn,
At the crack of dawn.

He can actually speak,
Even with his massive beak,
He has four friends,
They will be with him until the end.

Oh, Dragonray loves to eat pine cones,
He has his mind blown,
He will eat your crayons,
And interrupt matches so they can't play on.

Oh dear, can we stop Dragonray?

## Faramoluwa Ogunde (8)
Lime Academy Larkswood, Chingford

# Blobby

There was once a monster called Blobby,
He had a pet mondog called Flobby,
He had a friend called Feltch,
And another one called Squelch,
But one day, when he was ten
He abandoned both of his friends.
Blobby came and found me,
And then we both said, "Whee!"
Then, as we slid down the hill,
And perched along the windowsill
We saw that the world was made of ice cream,
So we both began to scream,
And rushed out of the door,
To eat the ice cream off the floor.
But then I woke up, it was just a dream,
But then I saw some peculiar steam,
Then I saw something that oddly,
Looked a lot like Blobby...

**Sophie Dolan (8)**
Lime Academy Larkswood, Chingford

# Textron Rap

There is a creature,
A girl and a boy mixed,
Its name is Textron,
And it comes from Rotis.

It's like this,
So repeat the track back,
Make it snappy,
And do it with a clap.

It can go through many stages,
But as you can see, it can evolve,
Textron is used for monster battles,
Up there on Rotis,
Where the strong monsters fight.

So that's the end of my rap,
I see you at the back,
But I doubt I'll be back,
Because I'll be on Rotis,
Thanks for listening.

## Mbangala Green (8)

Lime Academy Larkswood, Chingford

# My Monster Elexa

My name is Elexa,
I was born in a pearl,
Down on the ocean floor,
I have a fish-like tail,
And a head made of fluff,
When people see me,
They call me buff,
I may look pretty and clever on the outside,
But I'm warm and funny on the inside.

I have two friends,
Called Zoey and Emma,
We've been best friends since we were wee,
We care about each other,
And this shows as we love each other,
They skip and swim,
To my lovely, beautiful, beaming, amazing voice.

## Kalifa Dennis (7)
Lime Academy Larkswood, Chingford

# Boris From Kina

Boris from Kina is my best friend,
He can see all around because he has five eyes.

Boris from Kina likes to eat all my sweets,
He has so many teeth,
That he munches and crunches until they're gone.

Boris from Kina does not like anyone to see him,
So he turns invisible,
When someone comes into the room.

Boris from Kina has friends called Coola and
Zookerla,
And they do what they want.

Boris from Kina stays with me until I go to bed,
In the mornings, he plays with his friends.

## Honey Dye (7)
Lime Academy Larkswood, Chingford

# Mumlush The Mummy Troll

Mumlush the mummy troll,
Comes from deep down,
In one of the oldest pyramids in Egypt,
Made up of old, scruffy and smelly bandages,
Mumlush is very gross looking,
He stumbles and staggers,
Through the dry and stuffy corridors of the
pyramids,
His creaky footsteps and shrieks,
Can be heard as he prowls.

The 'evil' mummy horrifies explorers,
By staring at them through his tattered bandages,
With his bright, spooky eyes,
The lonely mummy then drags them down,
Down into his dark chamber,
For a nice cup of tea,
And a story about the good old times.

## Freya Sofia Mahomudally (8)
Lime Academy Larkswood, Chingford

# Deep Under The Dark Blue Sea!

Deep under the dark blue sea,
A fierce monster lurked mercilessly,
Hoping that one stormy day,
She'd find a friend to play with at the bay.

The days passed by to no avail,
And our monster got too frail,
She lost her hope and her desire,
To find a friend with a lovely smile.

But when the swirling sea cooled down,
And the stormy sky disappeared into the
background,
A shimmering and sparkling light,
Rose from the waves like a wild kite,
The monster had it in her sight,
And chased the light into the night...

## Daria Maria Ailenei (9)
Lime Academy Larkswood, Chingford

# My Monster And Me

Suddenly, I heard a sound,
A big, giant, scary monster in the backyard I found,
His skin was shiny, dark and blue,
As soon as I saw him, I got scared and flew,
He was as fat as an elephant, as tall as a giraffe,
He had red stripes around his neck like a scarf,
He was good and friendly to me,
Suddenly, I felt he'd come for me.

I used to be lonely but now I have a friend,
We play together whenever I can,
He has powers, he's invisible and a shape-shifter,
He himself has very unique characteristics,
He flies me high up in the sky,
He makes me happy when I cry.

## Ayaan Shaikh (8)
Lime Academy Larkswood, Chingford

# Can You See The Dragon?

Can you hear the dragon? The dragon, the dragon.
Can you hear the dragon? His roar is very loud.
Can you hear the dragon? The dragon, the dragon.
Can you hear the dragon? He's coming through the crowd.

Can you see the dragon? The dragon, the dragon.
Can you see the dragon? He's dancing on the street.
Can you see the dragon? The dragon, the dragon.
Can you see the dragon? He has claws on his feet.

Can you see the dragon? The dragon, the dragon.
Can you see the dragon? His tail is very long.
Can you see the dragon? The dragon, the dragon.
Can you see the dragon? His teeth are very strong.

Can you see the dragon? The dragon, the dragon.
Can you see the dragon? There's fire in his breath.
Can you see the dragon? The dragon, the dragon.
Can you see the dragon? He will frighten you to death.

## Michael Tsidi (8)

Lime Academy Larkswood, Chingford

# Rough Tough The Monster

He lives on a far island in the middle of the sea,
He is as fluffy as a teddy bear,
He is as scruffy as a gorilla,
If you saw him, you'd poo your pants,
If you saw him, you'd go as far away as Antarctica,
He will pull your hair out.

He is as tall as the Eiffel Tower,
He has yellow teeth like a crocodile,
He has long hair like a girl,
His breath smells like rotten cheese,
He has three tiny eyes,
He has stripes on his body,
He's a monster.

## Iman Muhammed (8)
Lime Academy Larkswood, Chingford

# Scary Mary's Poem

Beware, children, Scary Mary's here,
When the moon goes down,
Scary Mary's in the town.

Don't go near her,
She will bite you in one scoop,
She's really hairy and scary!

Her eyes are red,
Her ears are green,
She'll chase you with her stinky feet!

And if you don't open your door to her,
She will break the doors and windows,
And eat you in one foul swoop.

## Adam Tuc (8)
Lime Academy Larkswood, Chingford

# My Monster Friend

He is fluffy,
He is kind,
He is gentle,
But he drives me out of my mind.

He is hairy,
He is scary,
And those who don't know him should be wary.

He is clever,
He is smart,
He is special,
With a very big heart.

He is special,
He is kind,
A monster like him, you'll never find.

## Maya Juliana Bryan (9)
Lime Academy Larkswood, Chingford

# Doom's Day

Doom is made from the venom of a snake,
And frozen, blue ice,
He'll make you shake,
Believe me, he's not nice.

With the horns of a beast,
And the teeth of a cheetah,
He will eat you as a feast,
Because he's a meat-eater.

His eyes will make you scream,
When you're in a deep dream,
So remember to leave on your light,
Or he'll get you during the night.

**Samuel Barnard (7)**
Lime Academy Larkswood, Chingford

# My Marvellous Monster

There is a monster,
A marvellous and kind monster,
His name is Smig Bob.

He is very popular,
Smig Bob has so many friends,
Some aren't popular.

He always acts quite kind,
To everyone in the world,
He has a very kind mind.

Also, he's not from Earth,
He's from Saturn, it's boring there,
I'll go there if it's worth it.

**Dogan Dag (8)**
Lime Academy Larkswood, Chingford

# Match Days

I wasn't always a monster,
I just had a run of bad luck,
Ninety-nine years ago, I was run over,
By a big, black truck.
As I lay squashed in the road,
"He is gone," the people said,
But when I looked into the mirror,
I was a football monster,
With a body all covered in red.
Now I like to watch football games,
I am very tall,
My eyes are like balls,
I have five eyes and green wings,
With long blue horns and silver teeth.
In a crowd, I can be found,
I'm a good leader on match days,
I'm the friendliest monster you'll ever meet,
They sing out my name before every game,
They shout for Monster Pete.

**Tyler Allbeury (8)**
Lime Academy Larkswood, Chingford

# Big Monster Monty

Big Monster Monty went off to see the Queen,
Flowers in hand, the biggest he'd ever seen,
He felt excited and coy, but happy with joy,
He arrived at the palace in his monster truck,
He couldn't miss the Queen, that'd be just his luck!

Just then he saw the Queen,
Looking the best he'd ever seen,
Kind Monty made his way to the Queen,
She spotted him and he knelt,
And gave her the huge flowers.

## Callum Gill (8)
Lime Academy Larkswood, Chingford

# Blue's Adventure To Earth

I knew a monster and her name was Blue,
She came from a faraway planet called Moo.

One hot, sunny day, I went to school on the bus,
I didn't know she'd followed me until I heard all the fuss.

I made her hide for the rest of the day,
But the problems began when we started to play.

We were so excited to have our packed lunch,
But Blue's favourite food was our Monster Munch.

We opened our packed lunches and looked in surprise,
"Where are our Monster Munch?" we all cried.

We were all sad and thought it was a bad dream,
Blue was sorry so she bought us all monster ice cream!

## Jenna Ghelleahe (8)
Lime Academy Larkswood, Chingford

# The Cheeky Adventure

Cheeky was born in Monster Land in Norway,
She has pink, fluffy hair,
And is very, very thin,
She has a bow in her hair,
And wears it with flair.

Her friends sometimes tease her,
Because she only has one eye,
The other one's not there.

Cheeky is called Cheeky because she's so freaky,
She pranks all the others,
Who don't respect their mothers,
And teaches them a lesson,
From the one-eyed monster.

**Bailee Lewis (8)**
Lime Academy Larkswood, Chingford

# The Ender Monster

**E** xtraordinary little thing,
**N** aughty as a little toddler,
**D** ead in the underworld,
**E** yes are purple arrows,
**R** adical movements everywhere.

**M** r Scary,
**O** r,
**N** ot so nice,
**S** on of Hell in orange flames,
**T** eeth of an old man,
**E** normous, long hands,
**R** idiculous in every way.

## Daniel Pemaj (8)

Lime Academy Larkswood, Chingford

# Biggle

He is as small as a penguin,
He is as happy as the happiest man on Earth,
He is as friendly as a dolphin,
He is as furry and as spiky as the Gruffalo,
He can jump as high as a panther,
He can shoot lasers like Superman,
He is as fast as a flash,
He has excellent vision like an eagle,
His fangs are as sharp as Dracula's,
He has long, furry legs like a spider.

## Titot Guillaume (7)
Lime Academy Larkswood, Chingford

# Shape-Shifter

It was a gloomy night,
He felt a fright,
Something was happening,
No one knew,
So he looked at the news,
He fell to the ground,
And transformed into his imaginary reflection,
He turned into a reflection of a monster,
He knew he would stink,
And he had to blink,
And he started to grow,
And he started to glow...

## Sana Bhaiji (8)
Lime Academy Larkswood, Chingford

# The Small Kozikle

Kozikle is a monster that is good,
He lives in the sewers and is blue,
He has eight funky arms,
And four fat legs,
And a big, fat belly,
When he laughs,
His head is wobbly,
He has three eyes,
And three wobbly lines of hair,
Kozikle is a good monster,
I love him and he loves me.

## Tyra Alcin (8)
Lime Academy Larkswood, Chingford

# Kill Monger

Kill Monger is a large, beastly monster,
Who likes to live alone,
He is the apprentice of Thanos,
He uses his laser beam eyes,
To take out his enemies.

Kill Monger is working on his skills,
So he can take over the world,
With the help of his talons,
Thanos is teaching him how to shape-shift
stealthily.

**Quinton Lamptey (8)**
Lime Academy Larkswood, Chingford

# The Story Of Timmy Two-Face

Known as Timmy Two-Face,
The brothers were born as one,
They came flying from outer space,
And bad things began.

First, they robbed a jewellery store,
Then they hid in Larkswood Primary School,
But there, the students started a war,
And soon the terrible twins learnt the rules.

They suddenly stopped breaking the law,
They wanted to make Planet Earth their new
homeland,
So they said sorry and made sure everyone saw,
Then people welcomed them with a cheerful
marching band.

## Ata Ozan Cetin (8)
Lime Academy Larkswood, Chingford

# Scary Bob

Six red eyes staring at me from a shadowy cave,
Four long legs slowly walking closer to me,
Four wiggly arms trying to touch me,
Three scary heads with necks as long as trees,
He is wearing an awesome jacket,
It is purple and blue,
He has sharp, small spikes on his slim necks,
Four strong, almost invisible wings so that he can
fly.

## Austin Gustainis (7)
Lime Academy Larkswood, Chingford

# Devil The Evil

Devil The Evil is a monstrous monster.
He bellows viciously from deep inside the dark cave.
The rocky cliffs reverberate with the loud noise.

Devil The Evil is cruel and barbaric.
Intensely curious to catch a glimpse of the monster,
I stealthily creep near the mouth of the cave.

Devil The Evil wakes up from a deep slumber,
To cast his wicked, red eyes on my tiny frame.

Devil The Evil storms off,
I trudge through the deep sand,
I have never known such fright before.

## Aarman Malipatil (7)
Lime Academy Larkswood, Chingford

# My Monster

My monster has sharp claws,
She has no teeth in her oozing jaws,
My monster's eyes are green,
She has the most yellow fur you've ever seen!

My monster has bright pink antennae,
With golden wings to fly,
She's kind, sweet, daft and silly,
And likes it most when it's chilly!

**Florrie Irish (7)**
Lime Academy Larkswood, Chingford

# Naughty Monster

There is a monster,
Who was born in a muddy puddle,
He looks like a splodge,
And he lives underground.

He is called Merddy,
Whenever he walks,
He leaves stones everywhere.

His is a naughty monster,
And he smells like the sewer,
He causes mischief wherever he goes,
He is brown and his teeth are yellow.

He is rude but funny,
He tells everyone jokes,
But then tells them off,
He eats mud and is disgusting.

## Aiden O'Hara (8)
Lime Academy Larkswood, Chingford

# Monster, Monster

Monster, monster, under my bed,
With big, hairy hands and eyes of red.
Monster, monster, in my room,
You roar so loud, it makes my room boom.
Monster, monster, whenever I sleep,
I always wake up to a shriek.
Monster, monster, in my loo,
With stinky, blue poo.
Monster, monster, I see you cry,
Big, fat sobs but I don't know why.
Monster, monster, on your own,
Please don't cry because you're in my home.

## Josie Knight (7)
Lime Academy Larkswood, Chingford

# Grizzly The Monster

Grizzly, Grizzly, oh Grizzly,
She has five enormous, illuminated eyes,
Her skin is as spotty as a cheetah,
Her wings take her up to the clouds,
But she wishes that they could take her,
Back to her hometown.

On Earth, she has no friends,
But in her town, she has lots of friends,
Grizzly is good,
But she can be cheeky,
If I saw her, I would make friends with her,
Grizzly would be a nice friend.

## Ami Johnston (8)
Lime Academy Larkswood, Chingford

# Monty Monster

As monsters go,
I'm the friendliest you could know,
With a purple, fur coat and turquoise-blue eyes,
Horrible humans, I despise.

I am a unique yeti,
Oh and I do love my spaghetti,
I eat it in one slurp,
Followed by a great, big burp.

I have big, goofy teeth,
My house is underneath,
I can't stand bullies,
Oh, why can't they share their milk and cookies?

## Jaya Mander (8)
Lime Academy Larkswood, Chingford

# Mr Costa

I know a massive monster,
His name is Mr Costa,
He used to be a barista,
But now he's a gangster.

He is a monster king,
He's tall and scary,
He's much bigger than a fairy.
But he's not very hairy.

He's a giant,
And not very silent,
If he goes to a shop, he scares all the clients,
If he roars, you can hear him from miles around.

**Kaya Hamit (8)**
Lime Academy Larkswood, Chingford

# Scratchy The Volcano Monster

Scratchy was born at the edge of a volcano,
He has multicoloured fluffy fur,
He has brown rotten teeth and a hideous smile,
He has a bright yellow spirally tail,
He has no legs and he has four arms,
He also has antennae on his head,
Scratchy has lots of friends,
And once a year he goes to the top of the volcano,
To watch it erupt!

## Shiv Patel (8)

Lime Academy Larkswood, Chingford

# What The Monster Likes And What He Likes To Do

Monster, monster, do you want some food?
Monster, monster, what do you want to do?
Monster, monster, do you want some food?
Monster, monster, get some from the fridge.
Monster, monster, do you want to play a game?
Monster, monster, do you want to watch TV?
Monster, monster, are you feeling tired?
Monster, monster, say goodnight.

**Asia Karmelle Yau Philip (8)**
Lime Academy Larkswood, Chingford

# Louie The Monster

There is a giant, dark cave in the forest,
In the cave lives a fluffy, long-tongued monster,
He is horrendously gooey and his name is Louie,
He should live in a zoo as he looks like goo,
He has five lots of legs and scales on his head,
His horns are purple with spots and stripes,
And his fangs are every colour but white.

## Imogen Benjamin (8)
Lime Academy Larkswood, Chingford

# Red

I have a friend,
A monster named Red,
He often sleeps under my bed,
But if Mum's about,
And she starts to shout,
He hides in the chest full of toys,
My friend Red.

## Skye Spence (8)
Lime Academy Larkswood, Chingford

# Monster, Monster

Monster, monster, where do you hide?
Under my bed or in my head?
Monster, monster, what do you eat?
Snakes and cakes, or bears and pears?
Monster, monster, what do you look like?
All fluffy and blue, named Mr Cuddly and about six-foot-two!
Monster, monster, are you my friend?
Always and forever, until the end!

## Chris Frangou (8)
Lime Academy Larkswood, Chingford

# Four Arms

My monster is big and scary,
Like a lion but without a brain,
I would like to go to the Underworld on a train,
He lives there on his own because he is bad.
I would like to be friends with him because it
makes me sad.

## Shai Davis (8)
Lime Academy Larkswood, Chingford

# A Scary Monster

My friend Jeff is very scary,
He's purple and very hairy,
He's as spiky as a hedgehog,
And he jumps like a frog,
He's as fluffy as a cloud,
He shouts very loud,
He's a bit spotty,
His hair's very knotty,
He's very naughty,
He's very salty.

**Madison Drew Colley (7)**
Lime Academy Larkswood, Chingford

# Happy

He flew out of nowhere with a smile on his face,
He made a gloomy town a nice, happy place,
With his blue, fuzzy fur and his purple wings,
All the townspeople began to sing.

## Matthew Porter (8)
Lime Academy Larkswood, Chingford

# Amorter

He is a big monster,
He is hairy,
He lives under the stairs,
He snores like a bear,
He is loud,
He is messy,
But nice to be around,
He gets me into trouble,
And he does naughty things,
But I like being his friend.

**Ruby Treviss (8)**
Lime Academy Larkswood, Chingford

# Lily's Monster

At night, I sleep in the dark corners,
My vivid, bright colour,
My hair like a mop,
Causes shock and excitement,
But surely not fear,
It's me, Lily's monster,
Not a vampire that's near.

**Lily Rose Slack (8)**
Lime Academy Larkswood, Chingford

# Hell's Monster

Hairy face,
Got to be brave,
Acid spitting,
Human splitting,
Blood rushing,
Building crushing,
Isn't fun,
Children run,
He's colossal,
Not a fossil!

**Ari Ash (7)**
Lime Academy Larkswood, Chingford

# The Nick

The Nick was born on Mars,
He has five eyes,
He has big, sharp teeth like a T-rex,
He is quite stinky,
And has lots of legs,
He is naughty when humans are around.

## Reuben Carr (8)
Lime Academy Larkswood, Chingford

# Gloosa Goey

Gloosa Goey is funny,
But not a dummy,
He is yummy,
And as purple as a dark balloon,
He's from Planet Splat,
He's as squishy as a sponge!

## Louis Grant (8)
Lime Academy Larkswood, Chingford

# Hyper Venom: The Horrifying Hunt

Potion breaks, the horror rises.
This freak is whom everyone despises.
Poison slithers through the victim's body
and this horror likes nobody.
Its horse body pounces.
Its venom fills several ounces.
Its claws are like razors.
Its fork-tongue hisses.
Its terror dismisses.
Its tricks are so sly.
Your death is nigh.
Its fury increases so speedily.
When you go up against this you know your choice
was silly.
Its wickedness is unbelievable and is unbearable
when going up against this horrifying haunt.

## Samira Akhter (7)
Marion Richardson Primary School, Stepney

# Robbie Rebel Dream

What a sunny day, what's going on!
The trees are storming, houses are burning down,
people are dying.
This must mean one thing...
Robbie Rebel is here,
Oh no!
Everybody hide, the monster is here.
What monster?
Robbie Rebel, who's Robbie Rebel?
It's the monster that lurks around the village and
nobody could defeat it.
This evil, malicious creature kills anybody and
everybody.
It kills with strength and is very strong and plump.
I will be the hero of this village and kill the
monster.

## Maria Akthar (7)

Marion Richardson Primary School, Stepney

# Gobbly Monster

Gobbly Monster, Gobbly Monster
Fluffy and scruffy.
Gobbly Monster, Gobbly Monster
Likes to be all pretty.
Gobbly Monster, Gobbly Monster
Has lovely friends.
Gobbly Monster, Gobbly Monster
Is kind to everyone else.
Gobbly Monster, Gobbly Monster
Lives in a volcano.
Gobbly Monster, Gobbly Monster
Has a lovely family.
Gobbly Monster, Gobbly Monster
Has a lovely house.
Gobbly Monster, Gobbly Monster
Has a friend as a mouse.

## Aafia Bint Tufail (7)
Marion Richardson Primary School, Stepney

# Swiggy Is A Kind Baby Monster

Swiggy is really nice.
He also has head lice.
He likes to chew ice
Along with some rice.
Swiggy looks quite scary
Like his little sister, Mary.
He's also allergic to dairy
And his back is very hairy.
"Yawn!" Swiggy said,
"It's time to go to bed
Which is in my garden shed
With my favourite doll, Ted!"

## Abdullah Ahmad (7)

Marion Richardson Primary School, Stepney

# Scary Dream

Monsters' dreams are bad and mean.
Monsters snoring in bed, dreaming scary dreams.
Freddy is awake, reading books and having fun.
Jumping on the bed and sliding down the stairs.
Jumping on a mattress, playing with a ball and
watching TV.

## Idris Drici (6)
Marion Richardson Primary School, Stepney

# Pixelie

Pixelie had golden antlers,
And a coat that was as white as snow,
She had blue eyes,
She was born on Cubix and was wise,
And she grew and grew.

Pixelie flew off on an adventure,
And landed on Earth,
Her feet made no noise,
Or everyone would see how much she was worth.

She stood there,
Taking in all the new sights and smells,
I saw her and I thought to myself,
*I don't want these to go extinct.*

I went to Cubix in a wink,
And brought back another Pixelie,
Not long after,
Offspring was born,
Nowadays, they're called Deer,
And they've changed their ways.

## Holly Bai (10)
North Beckton Primary School, Beckton

# Oh Trody

Oh Trody was born in Monsterland,
He was very tall and big,
He walked along the street every morning,
To walk his precious dog.

In the afternoon, at one o'clock,
He went to see his funny, fat friends in the park,
Some were playing sports,
While others were building forts.

It was time for him to eat!
For dinner, he had mashed mango,
Hot hamburgers, big bananas and more,
Yum, yum, yum!

"Time to brush my teeth," he said,
Oh Trody brushed his teeth quickly,
He jumped into his large bed,
And sang a song for his dog,
They went to sleep together.

## Alexander Naydenov (9)
North Beckton Primary School, Beckton

# Arachnicat

My name? Well, they call me Arachnicat!
I am tabby, very hairy and really quite fat.

My mum is a spider and my dad is a cat,
And for some bizarre reason, my nan is a rat.

I have eight legs and I'm six feet tall,
I can climb up drains and cough up fur balls.

I like to chase mice, but squirrels are better,
I do my business in a tray of cat litter.

I have a pet fly and his name is Seb,
But he's not a big fan of the World Wide Web.

Some call me a monster and I'm okay with that,
Call me a friend, call me a buddy, call me
Arachnicat.

## Amélie Afia Owusu-Gyamfi (9)
North Beckton Primary School, Beckton

# The Day I Met Bob The Glob

Bob the Glob has lots of friends,
The fun never ends,
Bob the Glob likes grapes,
Bob the Glob keeps lots of capes.

He loves to have fun,
And see the sun,
Bob, Bob, Bob,
The,
Glob, Glob, Glob.

He loves to dance,
And never gets put in a trance,
Bob the Glob is green,
And he is not mean.

Bob the Blob is great at swimming,
And he's always winning,
He loves tennis,
Oh, how we love...
Bob the Glob!

## Sumayyah Rarih (9)
North Beckton Primary School, Beckton

113

# The Blob-Blob Monster

My monster has crazy hair,
And he is very pretty,
He has a big, fat body,
And is very scary.

He has three eyes,
And has four fluffy legs,
He's rarely scary,
He's fluffy, short and clever.

My monster eats spaghetti,
With ice cream, sweets and chocolate,
My monster has six friends,
And they are kind, nice, pretty, fluffy and giant.

I love him so much,
He is Blob-Blob, my monster,
He is very special to me,
He is my best friend.

## Ioana Potinteu (7)
North Beckton Primary School, Beckton

# Freaky Fred

He lived in the dark, treacherous land,
Of the underground,
*Stomp! Stomp!*
Freaky Fred comes this way,
People scream and people shout.

A shape-shifting, sly savage,
Who is anonymously amiable,
This 'fiend' tries hard to engage and interact,
I'm not lying, it's a fact!

Its black and red fur camouflages it,
With the black shadows and red flames,
If you can't see him, he's not to blame,
Freaky Fred is not a fiend,
He is surely a friend,
To those who are not mean.

## Faariah Malik (11)
North Beckton Primary School, Beckton

# The Mammoth Monster

I have this mammoth friend,
His name is Gaberbog,
He lives in a swamp,
And has horns as big as a hog!

I found him in the forest,
He was very lonely,
I went to him and said hello,
But Gaberbog couldn't understand me.

He ran to meet me,
We played tag and hide-and-seek,
And he got me.

Then I said bye to him,
And he went into a spaceship,
Where his mum and dad were waiting for him.

## Ziyad Shiraz Ahmed (8)
North Beckton Primary School, Beckton

# Stop The Tree Eater

The Tree Eater is destroying our planet,
The Tree Eater is dangerous for nature,
The Tree Eater is naughty and sticky,

We will trap the Tree Eater and destroy it,
We will need everyone to help capture the Tree Eater,
The Tree Eater comes at night,
We will wait in the dark and catch him,
And put him in a metal cage.

All together we can do it,
We can preserve our planet,
Save our Planet Earth,
Kill the monster Tree Eater.

## Rayan Thummanah (9)
North Beckton Primary School, Beckton

# Fuzzy Saves The Country France

Fuzzy was born in Turkey,
She was really fluffy,
She had a horn like a unicorn,
And had pink and red hair.

She was really kind and colourful,
She always helped people,
She was kind,
She was like a beautiful princess.

She left Turkey and went to France,
She needed to help people and make them happy,
She killed the horrible person with her laser beams,
It turned into dust!

"Hooray! Fuzzy's saved us!" the people said,
She smiled at them with her sharp teeth,
And her cute eyes.

Then she flew back to Turkey,
With her pink, sparkly wings

As she flew, she felt happy,
Happy that she'd saved France.

### Riana Rahman (9)
North Beckton Primary School, Beckton

# Ziggy

Ziggy is a clever monster,
He says, "Hola! Cómo Estás? "
His astonishing black eyes tell you stories of his
life.

He is usually quite calm but when he's mad,
He turns red, yellow and green,
Purple, pink and aquamarine.
He grows fangs and roars at you.

And you try to calm him down,
You say, "Ziggy, stop, will you?"
Ziggy calms down and relaxes.

## Maysa Popa Sayed (9)
North Beckton Primary School, Beckton

# Someone At School

Have you ever seen someone suspicious?
Well I have, when I was in Year 2
It was a very sunny day and the sky was blue,
There was a girl called Lizabaliba,
I asked her to be friends and play.

She was happy and said she'd play every day!
She said that she had come from a monstership,
And I was shocked when she said she was a
monster,
I almost choked on my food,
We were stronger together and we were proud.

## Maheru Uddin (10)
North Beckton Primary School, Beckton

# Fluffy

Fluffy is a monster,
From Monsterland Volcano,
He has three eyes,
And is all yellow.

He has four friends,
Each is very funny,
One has one,
Cute, little bunny.

Fluffy is clever,
I am too,
He likes cows,
That say moo!

## Lily Sobiye-Kotwica (8)
North Beckton Primary School, Beckton

# The Monster Squiggly

The monster was born on a farm,
He smells smoky and has eyes that glow,
In the dark, don't go outside,
You might see him with his glowing eyes.

This morning, it was strange,
He went to the beach and he saw me,
I thought he was bad,
No, no, no, he wasn't bad, he was good,
So I made friends with a good monster.

## Viktoria Strupnenska (9)
North Beckton Primary School, Beckton

# Spikester

Spikester had red and blue trousers,
He was hairy and scary,
He found himself in the woods,
He had black horns, a yellow face and spikes,
He was hideous and ran to the mountains,
He roared loudly until his friends came,
They said, "Roarity roar, here we come!"
They followed a wolf and ate it,
They had a good time.

## Nicolas Kulczewski (9)
North Beckton Primary School, Beckton

# Slimy Green Monster

The green, slimy monster has two big eyes,
He is friendly,
He goes to school,
He plays football with his best friend Jack,
He has a little brother and two big sisters,
He loves going to school because it's fun,
My slimy monster's name is Slimy Green Monster,
He is fun,
I like my slimy monster.

## Inaaya Ahmed (9)
North Beckton Primary School, Beckton

# An Amazing Alien

Once I met an alien,
He had blue eyes that glowed in the dark,
And had yellow skin which shone,
His name was Pikka,
He liked eating marshmallows with grass,
He had three eyes and one nose,
He liked doing weird sports,
He was great at maths,
Everybody said he was excellent,
He was terrible at English,
His hair was smooth,
He walked as fast as a cheetah,
He was eleven,
But his favourite number was seven.

## Manoor Ali Sajjad (8)
North Beckton Primary School, Beckton

# The Duster

Under your bed,
Lives The Duster,
Don't try to run,
You're not faster.

His teeth are so sharp,
Like a handful of daggers,
He will eat all your toys,
Say bye to your toy badgers.

He will mess up your room,
At the speed of light,
Cleaning it up,
Won't be a delight.

He will paint your walls,
Pink and black,
And boil your favourite doll,
Mr Jack.

## Weronika Miśta (10)
North Beckton Primary School, Beckton

# Monster, Here And There

Monster here, monster there,
It never stops,
It jumps everywhere, hop, hop, hop,
It walks with everyone.

Monster here, monster there,
It is like a rocket,
Zooming from place to place,
A very bad monster!

**Chantelle Oduro-Donkor (8)**
North Beckton Primary School, Beckton

# Friends With Freddy

In the purple world,
With the gentle people,
We could make Freddy,
He may be in your shed,
Or may just be in your bed,
He could be in your book,
Or even in your food,
He could be anywhere,
Just use your imagination!

## Mahmoud Bachrouch (9)
North Beckton Primary School, Beckton

# The Gentle Monster

There was a monster, I saw him,
But I think he was friendly,
He was helping the town,
He was a big giant,
But I knew he was a peaceful monster,
He looked like the Eiffel Tower,
His eyes were as blue as the sea,
His teeth were shiny like a mirror,
His personality was so good,
He made a lot of friends,
He announced he would host a grand party,
And everybody was invited.

## Qais (10)
North Beckton Primary School, Beckton

# Billy's Crazy Life

Billy walked down the silly street,
Filled with rabbits and aliens,
They were from a cheeky monster's imagination.

One day with a splash,
Billy saw a monster girl,
With enormous fake eyelashes,
Which Billy couldn't look at.

Her nose looked like a garden hose,
And every time she walked down the street,
She looked beautiful, like a sweet lollipop.

**Kamila Baran (9)**
North Beckton Primary School, Beckton

# Mini Monster Munch

Her name is Uniheart,
She loves to do art,
She is not harmful, she's peaceful,
She is cute and never on mute,
Her mum is Kelly,
Her mum loves jelly,
Her bunny is cute,
Rabbits are the best animals!

**Vyte Lukosiute (9)**
North Beckton Primary School, Beckton

# Smeagle The Gargoyle

**S** melly and sticky, I am.

**M** angy and hairy is my fur.

**E** ating bugs and insects as they're my favourite food.

**A** lthough I am nine feet tall, I am a friendly

**G** argoyle with big fangs and long talons.

**L** izard-like tongue with giant ears.

**E** yes all over my face. All six of them watching every one of you.

## Zayne Joaquin-Wayne Boggs (7)

North Beckton Primary School, Beckton

# Scary Mary

Scary Mary sat on a tree,
She blew the bubbles that everyone could see.

Scary Mary went to her lab,
Where she could do lots of crafts.

After that, she went for a swim,
To make sure that she stayed slim.

When the night came she realised,
That she had had the perfect day.

## Nicole Kamila Rompca (9)
North Beckton Primary School, Beckton

# Mr Stinky Monster

My monster is from Mars,
He only has two friends,
No one likes him apart from two people,
Stars above love him,
Trees melt when he's there,
Even flowers get ruined,
Running around in the plants is what he likes.

## Daniel (10)
North Beckton Primary School, Beckton

# Friendship Creation

Uni-Gem lives in Unicorn Villa,
Her fur is blue and white.
Never ever walk past her,
She will give you an unforgetful fright.
She jumps when she plays tricks.
People call her the Uni-Witch.
She shapeshifts and plays tricks
And the gullible queen fell for it.
Uni-Gem was out one day,
The monster queen was in her way.
Anger and frustration bounced in her mind,
What dirty trick will she find?
Uni shifted into a human,
Which all the monsters hate.
The queen screamed and fainted.
Uni-Gem was captured by the pixies.
She had many conversations
And was a witch no more.
Uni-Gem made something -
A friendship creation of gold.

## Rania Bendjebbas (10)
Selwyn Primary School, London

# The Gravedigger

In the night, the shadows begin to fade,
to the man who all shall obey.
Their families become poorer and poorer,
for their money is given to the man who shall lead
for evermore.
He laughs and cackles at people working as slaves,
as he begins to dig up more and more graves.
He lurks creepily underground,
as he slaps people in the face to make their heads
pound.
This mystery is still unknown to many who wonder
and still roam.
A hoodlum would fight but this one creeps,
upon people who continue to sleep.
An eerie black-eyed monster who is known to kill,
would sometimes take his prey and eat it for a
meal.
This monster is The Gravedigger.

## Zachary Grant (10)
Selwyn Primary School, London

# The Five-Eyed Fear

The Five-Eyed Fear is 0% cheer and it all started here.
He went to Testfest and a potion commotion led to furious fights and fear of heights.
He turned into a demon snake who is certainly not fake.
To prove it he had a website, but sadly no gigabyte.

After Testfest he destroyed towns, clowns and all around.
Five years passed and Testfest came round at last.
The Five-Eyed Fear went again to cause more tears.
Someone who was fed up with him put a potion in his lotion.
Another commotion!
Then a big cheer and no more Five-Eyed Fear!

## Joshua Hollows (8)
Selwyn Primary School, London

# Monster In My Closet!

There's a monster in my closet and he's scary.
I think he wants my wallet 'cause he's starving.
I creep across the floor to get near 'em,
so I can shut the door and stop his glaring.
He's really kinda big and big-time hairy.
He could snap me like a twig while he's sneering.
The door is coming loose from all his tearing.
He's got a real big tooth and a silver earring.
I'm rolled up in a ball and really screaming.
My mum turns on the light and... "Mum!"
Was I dreaming?

**Elisa Ali (9)**
Selwyn Primary School, London

# The Snake-Like Dragon

He's amazing, the one and only,
he's the best, he's the snake-like dragon!
He's a giant and if you try to tame him it's a stupid idea!
Do not go to him if you're his enemy,
he'll eat you up for tea!
Don't stick your head in his mouth for goodness' sake!
Don't even think to knock on his door,
he can swim, he can slither,
he flies, he's in disguise!
He's got a friend, Gridly Grun, who breathes fire as hot as the sun
and so does the snake-like dragon.

**Jason Vijayendra (7)**
Selwyn Primary School, London

# Orange Flames

This is me, Flames.
I am a giant, friendly orange big foot.
I live under the golden, beautiful, soft sand.
I always sing 'I love my little land'...
My favourite drink is fizzy orange Fanta.
When I've had too much of it
Flames, then causes lots of banter.
I like going invisible when I am feeling down,
I then cover myself up with a big, enormous gown.
I don't have many friends,
as they are all scared of my sharp, razor teeth.
So most of my time I spend beneath.
I'm a very clumsy monster who always has a fall.
I blame my five little eyes, being so small.
I sing so loud, waiting to be heard
as everyone beneath calls Flames a nerd!

## Roshni Pithiya (7)
St James' CE Junior School, Forest Gate

# In The Palace

In the palace there is Psycho Dragon who doesn't like gold.
If you ever go there, you'll never be cold.
If you don't understand just look at this.
It will burn you up and you'll be the colour gris.

In the palace there is an organism with high tech equipment.
We won't be having much enjoyment.
The organism will be happy every day
when we are crying every Sunday.

If this palace is giant it needs variety
or it will never reach the Vegetable Society.
Here is a plant that shoots beams.
We'll never be on the same team.

In the huge palace, a very sharp monster
who has a giant eye has a very cute cry.
It walks on its very long feet.
Whoever goes there turns to human meat.

In the humongous palace there is a human-like monster who wants to be a gangster.

Everything is in his hair
even a fierce bear.

Finally, something we know.
A Pikachu that doesn't grow.
It can easily be jealous
but that's all in the palace.

**Tej Paresh Gohil (8)**
St James' CE Junior School, Forest Gate

# Spectacular Cucumber

It has fangs, snake-like and five-eyed.
His name's Spectacular Cucumber.
It loves to eat your mum's pie.
It comes for your soul.
It's coming to the North Pole.

It loves to smell chaos and make it.
Look out for the underground monster.
It's a proper classic cucumber.
It's so early, so early to say it has long fangs like a vampire.
But one day there was a boy who gave him a wicked old smile.

They thought how fun it could be to put all the rubbish in one pile.
One person came from each village to complete the gang.
They came in different shapes and sizes.
They came from different cities in Monster Vania.

Some were short and hairy.
Most of them were hairy like little Mary.
They even had five eyes.

### Umar Hassan Mallu (9)
St James' CE Junior School, Forest Gate

# Bloody Jaw The Come Back

In the volcanic wind I saw a cute teddy
that said, "Night-night, sleep tight you're my little
friend tonight."
It was squishable and could change his eyes to
happy mode and scary.
I wonder what scary mode night be?

I took it to my dull, boring home.
In there I just moan and groan.
When I did my bed right
I sang him, "Goodnight."

The teddy was as stiff as a brick wall.
The teddy was going to fall.
The mighty, mischievous monster was on scary
mode!

Out of the blue, he turned me into pure blood.
I was like mud.
Then I said two words... "RIP! Yippee!"

**Kirsty Asamoah (8)**
St James' CE Junior School, Forest Gate

# The Magical Monster

Mermaf was born in the monster sea.
She has two ears like foxes' ears.
She has two fluffy owl wings, four vampire teeth,
a rainbow tail and a rainbow necklace.
She didn't have any friends because everyone
thought she didn't have any talents but she was
very good at magic because her necklace was
magical.
One day there's going to be a show and the people
need to vote.
Mermaf wanted to win.
Everyone was laughing but Mermaf didn't care.
When the show started none of the monsters got
40, they only got 9, 5, 4.
Mermaf had 40 and she won then everyone
became her best friend.
Mermaf was very happy then.

## Zeba (9)
St James' CE Junior School, Forest Gate

# The Cyclops Mushy Monster

The Crayzay Monster was born in a tub filled with soft, fluffy cotton candy.

Its skin colour was rainbow colours like in the sky.

He was as clumsy as a boy falling every second.

At night he likes to write with the light.

The Crayzay Monster's teeth were as blue as the sky.

The Crayzay Monster lived in Monstay World.

Every time he smiled everyone would run a mile.

In his town, there's a lot of pollution so he tried to find a solution.

The Crayzay Monster met another boy, Bould who changed his world.

Their bond was as strong as a brick wall.

Now in the night, they write without no light.

## Nisha Kaur (9)

St James' CE Junior School, Forest Gate

# Monster Madness

Last night there was a monster in my bed.
She had two sharp teeth, two red eyes and four
slimy legs.
She was fluffy and woofy, hairy and naughty.
She will eat my socks and then grow some spots.
She took me out on a monster madness adventure.
We made a new friend with a cute, fluffy bear with
lots of hair.
My mum walked into my room to check how I was.
She looked once and looked twice but I was
nowhere to be seen.

Two weeks later she suddenly found me in my
monster mad bed because Bon Bon the monster
was early but I managed to get back home.
Now my name is Monster Sisi.

**Sienna Sylvia Byne (9)**
St James' CE Junior School, Forest Gate

# How Many Types Of Monsters Are There?

Monsters - some can be fluffy and some can be happy.
Some are cute and can turn as small as a newt.
They can be tired or really admired.
They can be funky or have a name like Hunky.
After all they can be anything, maybe like a trendy thing.
Some can never break a bone and it's not like a home.
But there's a special monster almost like a petal monster.
And there's a monster that's blue but it's not as sticky as glue.
There was a monster with no brain but carried around a candy cane.
Monsters are not all the same but are a great combination.

## Kayla Monica Monteiro (9)

St James' CE Junior School, Forest Gate

# The Junk Man

This is all about a monster that loves cake
He goes to the shop to get himself some steak
His family tells him to get water from the lake
He often goes to his cousin's house,
His name is Jake
He gets shoes that are normally fake.

He likes to eat junk food
The monster went swimming then sunk
The monster told his dad there is no end
So they both talked and they always send.

He put a smile on his face
People took it a mile
He walks in style
In his work he took a while
In his kitchen he was a tile
He always smiles.

## Daddy Dampha (9)
St James' CE Junior School, Forest Gate

# Monster Friends

One day there was a man called Gooky
who was very oozy and puky.
He had a lot of friends
who would always find gems.
Today he wanted to find different people
who were very evil, to change their ways for days.

He went to a suspicious house
that looked like a mouse in a couch.
When he went inside he saw angry guys
who looked like they had run miles on tiles.

He found a special girl
that rocked his world.
He changed her mind
so he could be a thoughtful guy.

## Gabriella Mumenu Kinduku (9)
St James' CE Junior School, Forest Gate

# I Am Here

There was a monster named Blue
but he wasn't as sticky as glue.
He had a friend called Bill
and he never gave up, he was always still.
One day Bill wasn't chill.
Blue said, "I'll help you."
Blue brought him some ice and gave him some
cool glue.
Bill ate the ice and drank the cool glue.
Then Blue said, "Come on Bill, we'll go up the hill."
Bill said, "Thank you."
Blue said, "Oh dear, you never need to fear 'cause I
am here."

## Siyona Paliwal (9)
St James' CE Junior School, Forest Gate

# It's Coming For You!

My monster is a sucker.
Its nickname is Cutter.
It can bite your legs and suck your blood.
Careful where you go, it's coming for you!

This was my nightmare,
I was sitting in the night
And thinking about the mighty monster.
Suddenly I saw a shadow in the light.
It was a human size,
Probably bigger than me.

It came closer and closer.
I had nothing to do.
It was surrounding me.
I knew for a fact I was going to die today!

## Hajar Bennebri (9)
St James' CE Junior School, Forest Gate

# The Way Of Uganda

"My brother, do you know the way?"
"No, my brother."
"We need to find the queen."
"Let's find the queen!"

Know the way, know the way,
As we are the Knuckles Squad
And we need to find the way!

We click our tongues as we follow the queen
Because only she knows the way
And she will take us back to our homeland
By making a tunnel and we shall know the way.

## Matyas Sarosi (9)
St James' CE Junior School, Forest Gate

# Boby Goes To Sleep

A small ball.

This small ball had two other sticks which act as legs.

It had two other sticks which acted as hands.

This fluffy, scary thing is not allowed to see spots.

The reason is that if he does he can fall asleep and never wake up.

As you know Boby is very naughty.

He wants to sleep but he does not want his mum to chop his feet so he hides them and falls asleep.

He is now deep asleep and can never wake up.

## Yahyah Islam (9)

St James' CE Junior School, Forest Gate

# Sour Soul

Down in Bysterian,
lives a creature called Sour Soul.
She spreads bacteria
and thinks she's superior.

She's claimed cute
but she thinks she's puke.
Her friends are nice
but she doesn't appreciate them.

She is a disease
and causes mayhem.
"Cheers to Sour Soul
for she is the most mischievous one here,"
scream and shout the villains.

## Aisha Saddiq (9)
St James' CE Junior School, Forest Gate

# Monster Madness

Scully Mully was as dark as night
His teeth were sharp and bright.

One look will scare chills down to your pants
As he will count to nine.

Through all the chaos he only wanted a friend
In this town with only one end.

So Scully Mully got a friend in the very end.

He ended the story with a very big smile
When he would smile you would go another mile.

## Fabian Hurduc (8)
St James' CE Junior School, Forest Gate

# Chickenbeamculupy

Once I met a creature called Chickenbeamculupy.
It shot one with her chicken-beaming eyes as if I
was its enemy.
His mischievous smile makes me think that she is
an evil creature.
Her body is as puffy as a popcorn.
She's fluffy and poisonous.
How cute she is but just deadly.
When she's angry her eyes turn red and shoot
fierce, deadly lava.
You wouldn't want to go near!

## Favour Odunola Akinwande (9)
St James' CE Junior School, Forest Gate

# My Unicorn

My unicorn can fly so high
She's in space
She's magical like a genie
She is as clever as a cat
Mischievous like a puppy
My unicorn is as invisible as slender Superman
Is short but cute
No one can replace her even if you try
She loves doughnuts especially chocolate
That's why I love her
She's the only one that knows me.

## Raenella Ofori (8)
St James' CE Junior School, Forest Gate

# Dogslime In Disguise

The slimy dog smells like a wild hog.
As the wind blows
he holds onto his wheel as he relies on it to live.
As the suspicion of the fallen assassins grow
another rises up from his shoes
but he doesn't know what to do!
It is marvellous and all,
but is hard to carry on this life.
Can he live a lie?
Well, that's the life of Dogslime.

## Tayyab Ahmed Hussain (9)
St James' CE Junior School, Forest Gate

# The Monster Of Mysteries

The Monster of Mysteries' teeth were as yellow as the shiny bright sun.

His skin was as green as the greeny grass.

His horn was as sharp as a needle.

The monster was camouflaged in the dark night sky.

His teeth were so sharp it would send chills down your spine.

Beware for night, close your windows tight and lock your doors!

## Sara Abdo (9)

St James' CE Junior School, Forest Gate

# Roseyboo's New Pet

Hello my name is Roseyboo and I live on
Planet Bong.
I really want to visit Hong Kong.
My mummy bought me a lava fish as a pet
and it always crept and crept.
It was as red as my cousin's skin
and my fish had a soft, fabulous fin.
My fish shoots lava if it is angry
so I give it air on the bumpy balcony.

## Henriqueta Djalo (9)
St James' CE Junior School, Forest Gate

# The Story Of Bob

I was born on a ring of Bing, propelled to sing.
I was scary and hairy like a bear.
I had a heart like a hand ready to grab a piece of butter.
I was as short as a box.
My body made of spring locks.
I had a smelly belly and tentacles made of jelly.

## Anayet Noor (9)
St James' CE Junior School, Forest Gate

# The Orange Monster

Last night I saw a monster with
Two sharp teeth,
Orange skin
And his face was like a dragon.
He has fluffy fur
And he took me to the Five-Eyed Dragon Volcano.
In the morning I woke up,
I was in my room and the monster was not there.

## Miftahul Islam (9)
St James' CE Junior School, Forest Gate

# The Lazy Crazy Wozza

The Lazy Crazy Wozza was as scary as a vampire.
His teeth were as sharp as the tip of a pencil.
When he would smile he would go another mile.
Fuzzy Wuzzy spent his day like a dog with no bone
And ended up changing his world.

## Mohammed-Quam Temitope Balogun (9)
St James' CE Junior School, Forest Gate

# Monster Legend

Planet Earth is in great danger,
They need Monster Island to send a saviour.
They call a monster who is brave and strong
So Fire Crusher came along.

The people on Earth are scared and shaking.
Skull Crusher, the evil dragon was misbehaving.
He had locked the humans in a cage,
Wanting them to be his slaves.

Now Fire Crusher had a plan
But he needed his best friends,
Man Crusher and Flying Crusher.

They flew around to make Skull Crusher dizzy
Then Fire Crusher jumped out to spray him with
fire balls.
Once Skull Crusher was stuck
The humans were free.

Then they all cheered for Fire Crusher,
For he was a good monster indeed!

## Nathan Precilla (8)
St John Of Jerusalem CE Primary School, Hackney

# Monster Crusher

My monster is from Claw Crusher Island.
It has four arms and in one second it can poison
you with one shot.
He has three spines and a hundred spikes
so he doesn't get tickled and he doesn't get killed.
His weakness is the sun but he is good at climbing
especially Mount Everest.
He is good but he gets angry when you say go
and he is good at running, he has three modes.
The first mode is 'running very quickly' mode,
the second one is 'heavy mode'
and the final mode is 'fighting mode'.
He has two transforms.
The first one is a car and the second is a boat.

## Wen-Jie Zheng (8)
St John Of Jerusalem CE Primary School, Hackney

# Beware Of Lava Diver

Stay away from the skin-killing monster,
He will use fire and you will burn slowly.
"Water, water, you need water,
Quickly or you're doomed!"
Well, you are once you're caught by The Lava.
Make sure you have lots of water.
Stay away from the skin-tearing monster,
He will use fire and you will burn quickly.
"Water, water, you need water,
You need it or you're doomed!"
It tears your skin and your blood comes,
Dripping like a tap
And your skull is the only thing left of you!

## Chinedu Duru (8)
St John Of Jerusalem CE Primary School, Hackney

# Fear

Fear, fear,
Oh dear, oh dear!
These bugs just climb upon your skin.
Not caring they're from Lazy Lamb.
Not caring for anything,
Just climbing on your skin.
They bite and bite and look around
And if they see something scary
They say, "Stop! Don't go there, please stop!"
And send that message to your brain.
But you can say no, you can give in
But it's your time to choose...
Believe or not, just choose and you'll be fine!

## Edward Skrine (8)
St John Of Jerusalem CE Primary School, Hackney

# Green, Gooey Monster

He's a green, gooey monster
Who lives in Monsterland
He has so many friends
But will he have them forever?
The green, gooey monster is good
But maybe secretly he eats people
So if you see this green, gooey monster
Be careful, he might eat you!

**Tahiya Ahmed (8)**
St Matthias CE Primary School, London

# Darren Destroys Royal Wedding

Darren is a monster
A monster as naughty as could be
Even when he needed a pee.

One day, on Saturday the 19th
Darren felt miserable
As miserable as could be
He remembered the royal wedding
He packed his bag with all sorts of bedding
Including things for the royal wedding.

He bought a blue stick
Which he licked.
Darren jumped from pocket to pocket
Until he was at Prince Charles,
Then to the Queen's pearls
Up upon her head.

Sticking her hat to her head
Prince Philip saw him
And tried to catch him

But only ended up slapping his Queen.
"Ouch!" cried the Queen.
Which caused a riot,
Which stopped the wedding from carrying on.

On the first news
It was hard to lose.
The sight of Darren on it.
Ever since then
People have tried to find him
But they could not even see a limb.

But at Darren's house
He was busy, busy sitting on a chair,
A chair which was the diamond from Meghan's tiara
Which is covered in Harry's hair
To make it more soft to sit on.
And Darren lived happily ever after
But the royal family did not
Whilst he is scootering around
On his one wheel leg.

## Mary Luggie (9)
Whittingham Primary Academy, Walthamstow

# Revenge Of Glory's Magic

A young unicorn named Glory,
quite attractive as you see.
But when the witch called Willow came to visit
everything was a horrible fright!
With all of Glory's might
she wanted to visit this witch named Willow.
But first must get some advice to try to get her
legal right.
With a ray of hope in her soul
she pays the wizards a visit.
The three wizards have a spell in mind
but will need great power.
A powerful push and Glory turns to something she
feared!
A bloodthirsty vampire and in the blink of an eye
Glory is transported to the realm of black magic,
belonging to Willow the evil, stone-hearted witch.
Dangerously bouncing back and forth spells of
friendship.
Glory plunges straight into Willow's skin but
nothing happened.

After six plunges and six hits from Willow
Glory feels depressed about having no magic.
Glory gives it one more strike and tears Willow's
pale, wrinkly skin.
Collapsing breathless in a heap of blood, lay
Willow, dead!
Like a miracle, everything turned back to normal.
Glory's magic was restored back into her horn
and she was looking fabulous again.

## Maimuna Ali Mohamed (10)
Whittingham Primary Academy, Walthamstow

# The Deadly Danger

The Deadly Danger was truly deadly.
For sure he was not friendly.
His intention to destroy the universe was grave.
Nobody was safe, not even in a cave.
The To Kastr could shoot cosmic and plasma rays.
One horrendous day was about to come.
It was the end for everyone!
The Deadly Danger was out, destroying planets,
he came to Earth and shot a cosmic ray.
Everyone was doomed that day.
Nobody would survive...
Nobody would remain alive...

He destroyed Earth and grinned.
The Deadly Danger was about to complete his goal.
He shot a ray that was plasma and cosmic at full power.
*Whoosh!* He shot and then, *bang!*
The universe was destroyed...
Gone forever as well as everything inside it...
He won!

## Mohammod Dua Mahmud Unnoto (9)
Whittingham Primary Academy, Walthamstow

# Joy Monsters

Jaw-droppingly friendly monster arrived at my
house.
Oh her voice sounded like a mouse
Yet she loved her voice.

Milly was her name, she came from a planet called
Joice.
Of course she didn't speak our language.
Now I taught her, her favourite word was cabbage.
She had furry, yellow skin.
The planet she came from was shaped like a tin.
Everything I said was just what I was told.
Really she just ate mould.
Surprisingly I loved her.

Amazingly her fur was yummy.
Really I heard her say 'lummy'.
Ew, her fragrance was weird.

Funny is how you would describe her.
Unhappily she left me.
Really I did miss her, I was lonely soon.
Yes I was sitting on a tree all lonely, looking at the
moon.

**Chloe Alexandra Bray (9)**
Whittingham Primary Academy, Walthamstow

# Friendly Monster Who Eats Children

Due to the midnight scare
The bad dream comes, a bear
There comes the mayor
There is no one to bare.

*Bang!* Fluffy wool comes from under the bed
The lights are red
The fur had no head
The fluffy wool comes from under the bed

It had fangs sharp as a razor
It had an eye which looked like a taser
I have never seen anything
Like that before.

*Bang!* Fluffy wool came from under the bed
The lights are red
The fur had no head
The fluffy wool comes from under the bed

Due to the midnight scare
The bad dream comes, a bear
There comes the mayor
There is no one to bare.

## Ellie-Mae Carroll (9)
Whittingham Primary Academy, Walthamstow

# Houndar

*Roar! Bang!*
A monster... a huge one...
A massive one.

Big, humongous, ruthless!
Lands in Japan.
Daggers as teeth,
Crushing, crunching,
*Ping!*

His blood-red eye spots me,
Sees me,
I feel paranoid,
Petrified, terrified,
All I can do is hide.

It's like a scary ghost ride,
It rampages towards me,
Stomping on everything,
On everything in its way,
Though I get away.

Dragon-like attitude charging,
As powerful as the sun,
Yet it doesn't shine,
It takes people's lives
As it flies back to Necrozma.

## Richard Khalil Minott (11)
Whittingham Primary Academy, Walthamstow

# Holohulu Pants

On the way to school I met a monster.
It looked just like a prankster.
With a long tail to its ear
I asked it, "Is that your gear?"
He said, "No!"
"Well," I said, "hello."
I was trying to look friendly
but he looked elderly.
He was really mean.
He said I looked like a stinky bean!
"Excuse me Sir, I didn't mean to make you angry!"
But he said that he was hungry.
Once he went on an adventure
but he accidentally killed a benchture.
Although he's from Monster Booville
he will still build a windowsill!

## Antonia Maria Avram (9)
Whittingham Primary Academy, Walthamstow

# The Alien

There was once an alien from Chingford
Who really liked to eat
He ate, he ate, he ate, he ate
And then he went to sleep
But then he found a person
Who ate and ate like him
He asked to be best friends
But he said that he was dim.

When he went home
He decided to eat
But in the fridge
There was a bloke called Pete
He walked to the sofa
To watch TV
But in the middle of the show
He had to do a pee!

The next morning, he went to the station
But when he got there,
There was no transportation!

**Daniel Brace Carmona (9)**
Whittingham Primary Academy, Walthamstow

# Friendship Forever!

One scorching hot day
An adorable monster crept a long way.
She had skin like a sapphire
And large, black, beady eyes.
Her name was Love.
Unfortunately she had no friends
But as she turned to go to school
Another monster pushed her to the filthy floor.
She felt dejected.
A hand touched her back.
A gentle, soft touch.
It was a human.
"Can we be friends?" Love cried.
"Yes," the girl declared.
She was a warrior -
A hero and Love's new friend!

## Summer Yakici (10)
Whittingham Primary Academy, Walthamstow

# Getting To Know Mrs Evela

Hello, I am Mrs Evela
I come from outer space
I don't like monsters who sweat
But when it comes to me
They think I'm a threat.

I love to eat, eat and eat
But eventually, I have to go to sleep
I never thought you could leap
In water so deep
I don't need to go to school
'Cause I'm too cool, doh!
And don't even call me a fool!

Whatever your name is
I'm sure it is lame
And hey, do you want to play a game?

**Taybah Zainab Shah (9)**
Whittingham Primary Academy, Walthamstow

# Murder At Dawn

I'm the hound of doom
I'm a mini assassin
And when the time is right
I'm coming through the bed, crashing.
I'm a killing hound
And I'm always ready for a bloody assassination.

I scratch the bed and use toys as blissful bait.
I throw precarious grenades that explode.

Never remove my mask
Because I'm an abomination.
I'm from the military and I am a creation.
Never wake up because I'll be there.

**Nathaniel Marcus Kai Thomas (10)**
Whittingham Primary Academy, Walthamstow

# The Giant, Friendly Monster

My monster is very ugly
and he nearly looks like a lobster.
He plays very fast and he's never last.
He jumps up and down like a silly old clown.
And because he jumps so hard
he nearly breaks the town.
He likes to eat lots of meat.
He likes to sneak like a mouse looking for cheese.
He might look a little bit scary
but it's not him, he's quite a bit hairy.
Everybody loves him but he just needs to get slim.

## Emmanuel Chibuike Chinedu (8)
Whittingham Primary Academy, Walthamstow

# Frizz The Monster

My monster is from a planet called Fazzy.
His favourite food is bazzy.
We are best buddies.
He is a good monster.
An adventure we go on is for us to know.
I can go to his planet.
The first time I saw him I thought it was a dream.
It was the best day ever.
He was so fluffy and cuddly.
Nobody liked him,
I am the only one that liked him.
He was amazing,
He was good to cuddle at night, like a teddy bear.

## Erhan Bulut (8)
Whittingham Primary Academy, Walthamstow

# Deadly

I was born in a volcano bursting with fire
with red glowing eyes, blue skin,
fire tail and sharp claws.
I am dangerous.
I will scare people with my fire.
You don't know what I can do to you
I will make you cry so much,
I will make everyone cry with my fire
so you should stay away from me.
I hate humans like you
and my name is Deadly.
I will scare you now
so you should stay away from me.

## Laurynas Vaicenavicius (9)
Whittingham Primary Academy, Walthamstow

# The Slimy Monster

There is a scary monster called the Slimy Monster.
He lives in a scary, dark forest.
He is as stinky as rubbish.
His favourite food is a wolf pizza!
He looks like a red, scary dragon.
His fire is like dark blue.
His teeth are ginormous.
His nails are so sharp,
They can cut through metal.
He is the strongest monster you have ever seen.
If you ever see him don't forget to scream!

## Ali Dereli (9)
Whittingham Primary Academy, Walthamstow

# The Friendly Sweet

He is absolutely so sweet
Never ever a creep
Bangs vibrate in my ear
Extreme tingly feelings give me fear
Looking in the freezing freeze
I see a frozen monster
Its name is Sweet 305.

## Rehan Mohamed (9)
Whittingham Primary Academy, Walthamstow

# YOUNG WRITERS INFORMATION

We hope you have enjoyed reading this book – and that you will continue to in the coming years.

If you're a young writer who enjoys reading and creative writing, or the parent of an enthusiastic poet or story writer, do visit our website **www.youngwriters.co.uk**. Here you will find free competitions, workshops and games, as well as recommended reads, a poetry glossary and our blog.

If you would like to order further copies of this book, or any of our other titles, then please give us a call or visit **www.youngwriters.co.uk**.

Young Writers
Remus House
Coltsfoot Drive
Peterborough
PE2 9BF
(01733) 890066
info@youngwriters.co.uk